D0272801

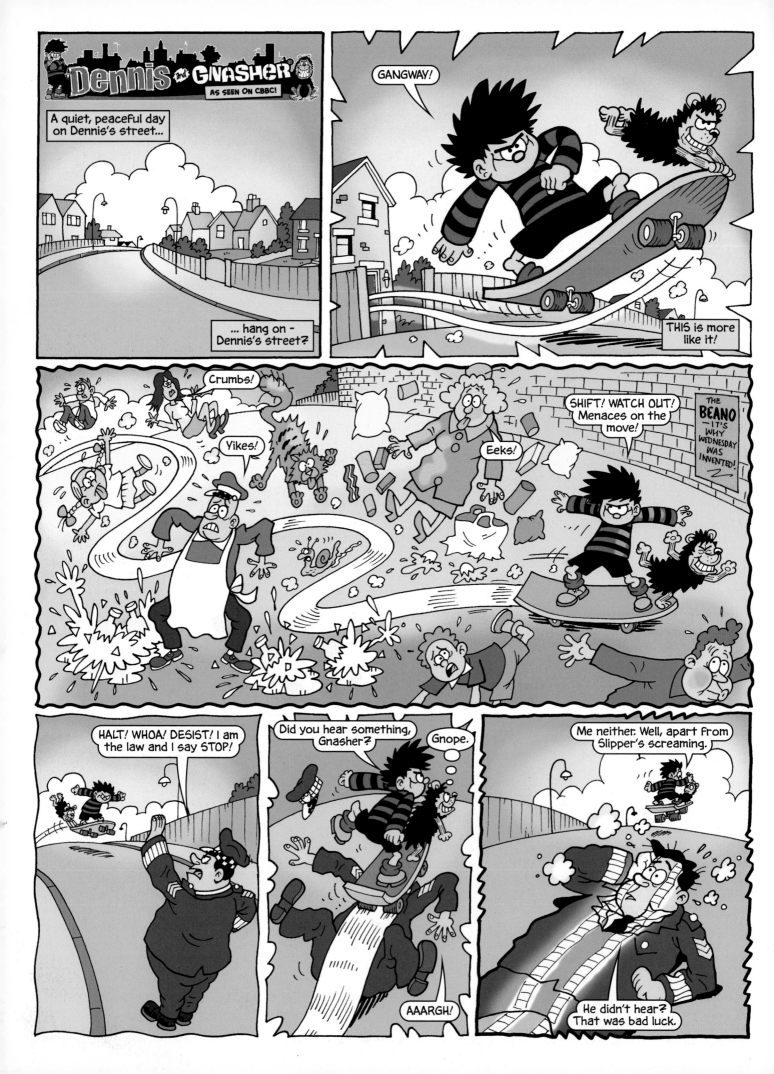

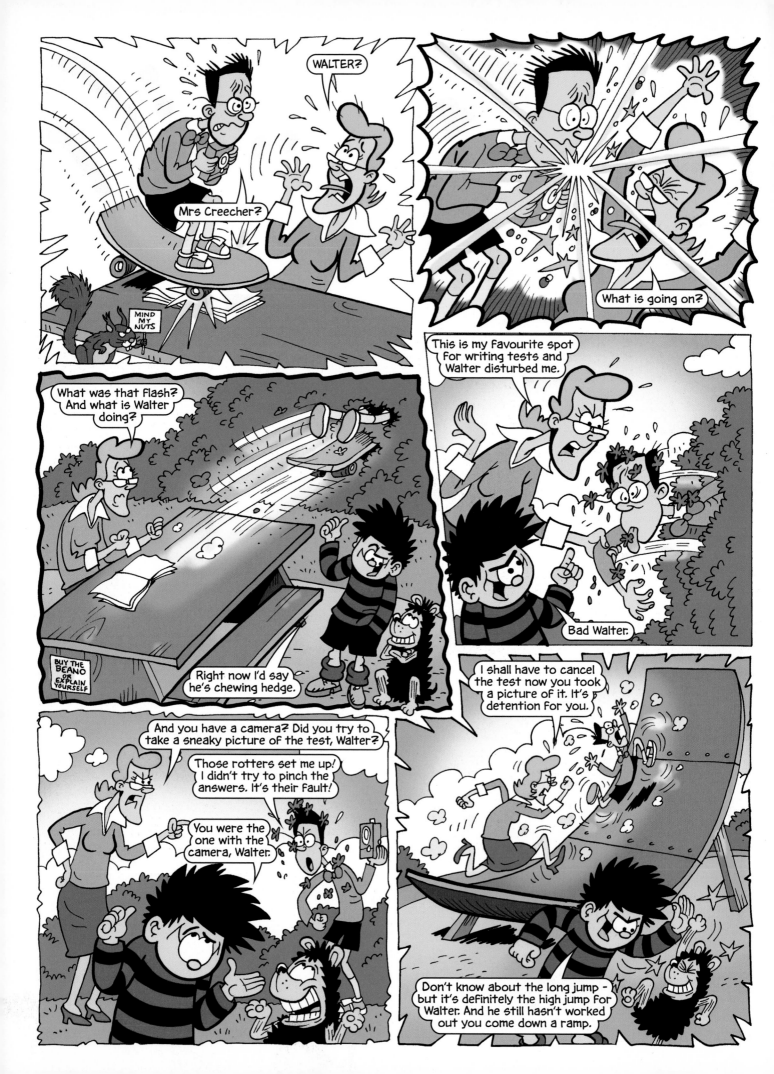

REVOLTING RHYMES

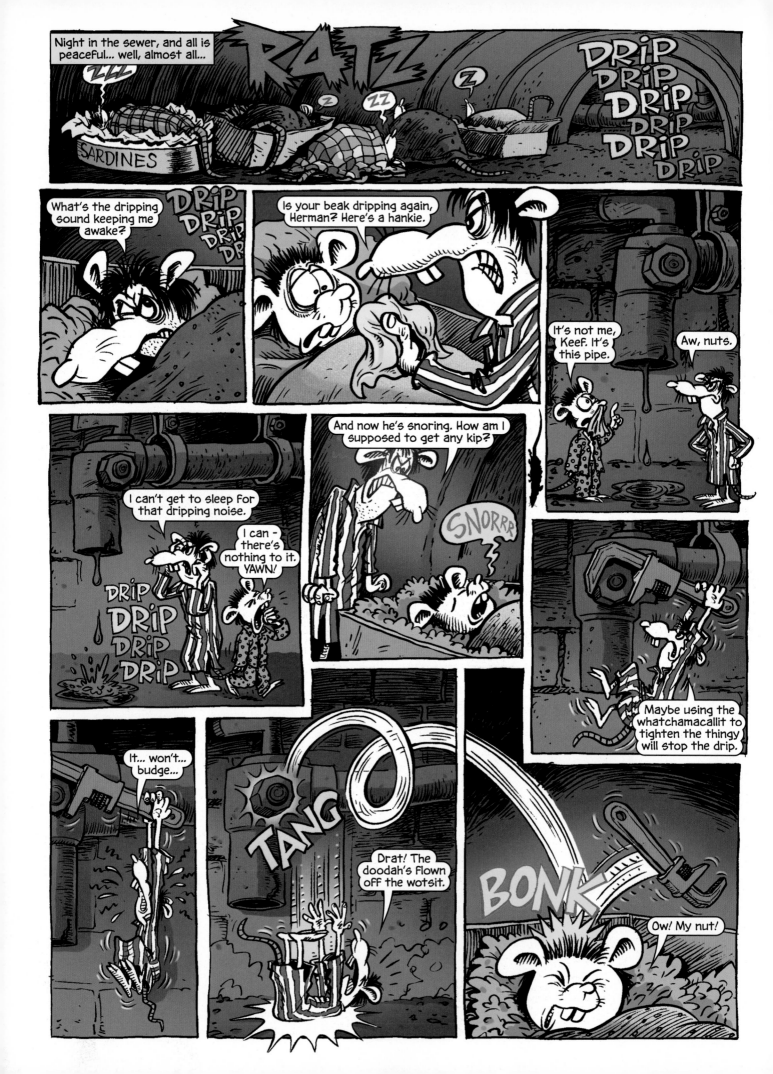

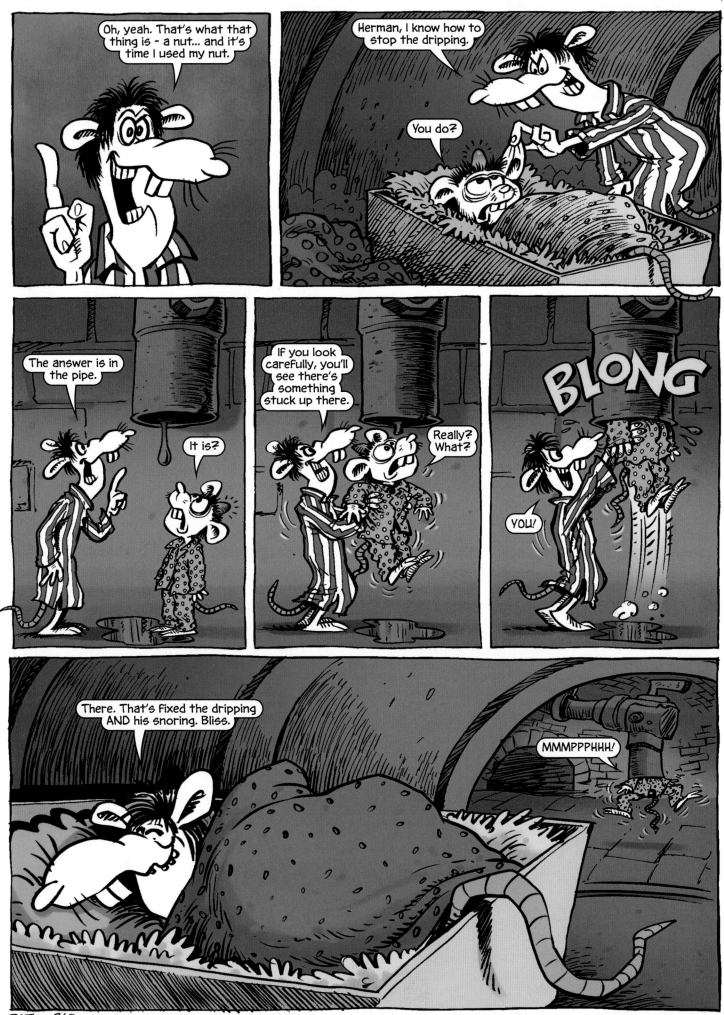

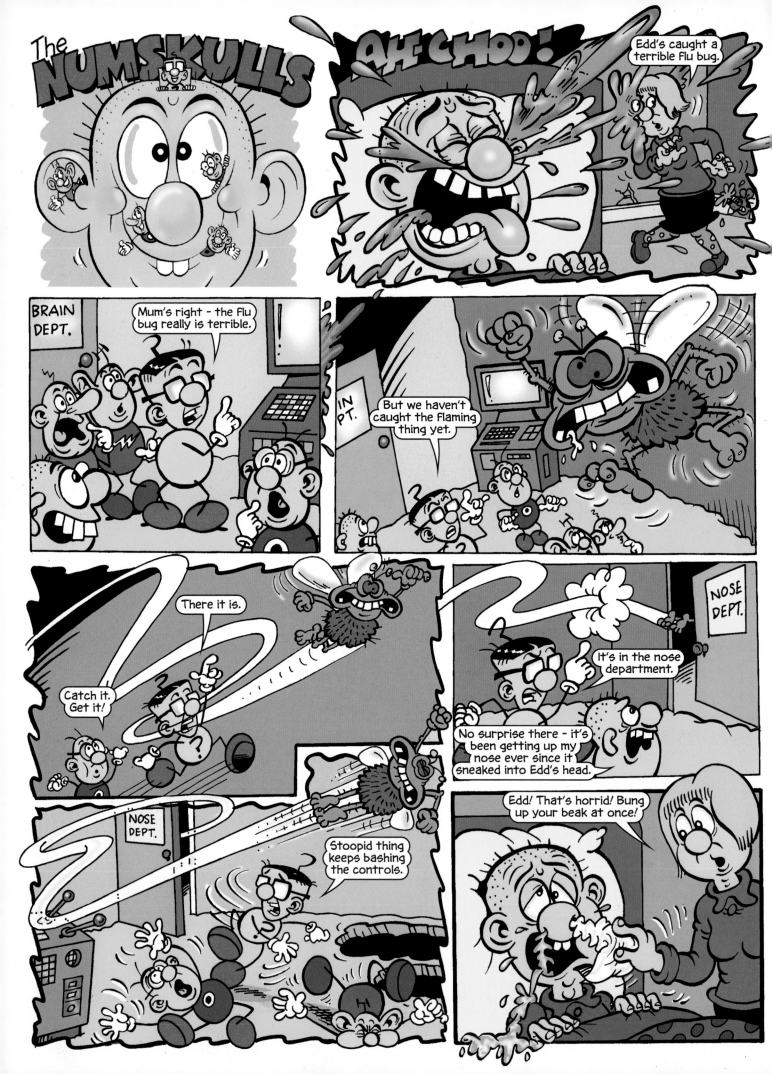

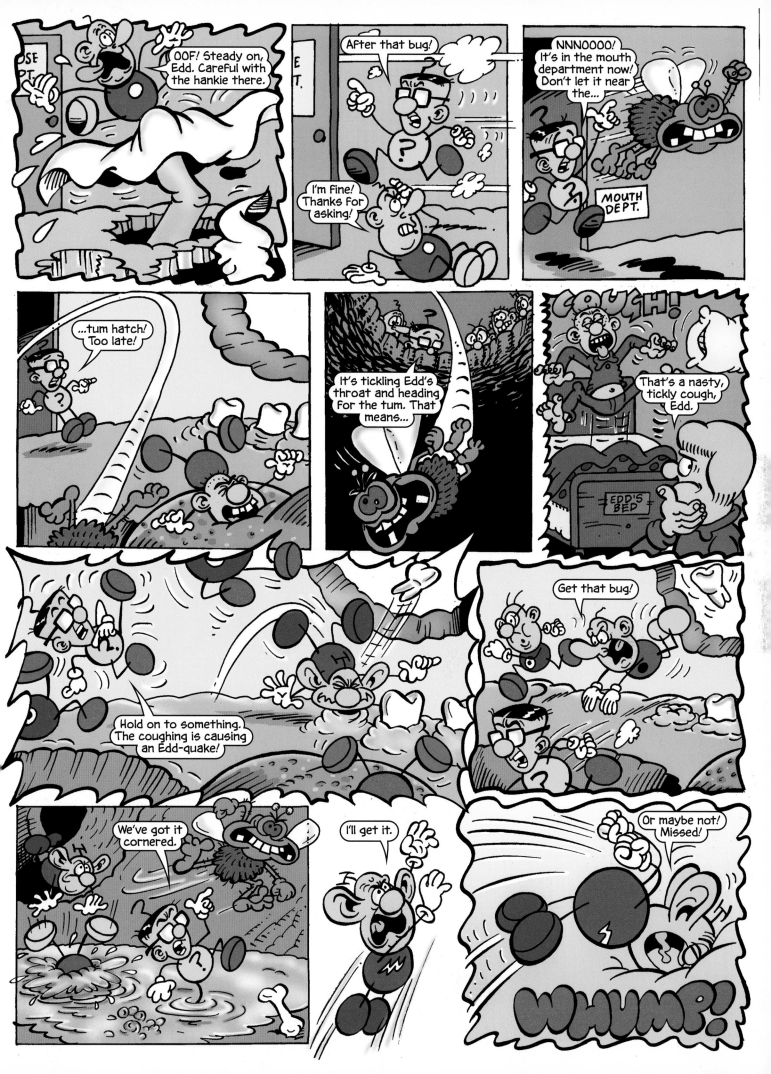

GNASHER'S

Us dogs love a laugh. Gnadmittedly, that usually involves chasing cats — that really makes me laugh. But I like a joke, too. Here are some of my favourite dog jokes.

What do you get if you cross a dog with a phone? A Golden Receiver.

Why don't dogs talk to their feet? Because it's rude to talk back to your paw!

Why do dogs wag their tails? Because nobody else will do it for them!

HOWLERS!

Why do dogs bury bones in the ground?
Because they can't bury them in trees!

What happened when the dog went to the flea circus?
He stole the show.

What do you get if you cross a sheepdog with a rose?
A collie-flower!

Which dog wears glasses?
A cock-eyed spaniel.

Why did the dog chase his tail?
He was trying to make both ends meet.

What kind of dog did Dracula have?
A bloodhound!

Where does a Rottweiler sit in the cinema?
Anywhere it wants to.

Heard about the dog that only ate garlic?
Its bark was much worse than its bite.

Why do you have to be careful when it's raining cats and dogs?
You don't want to step in a poodle.

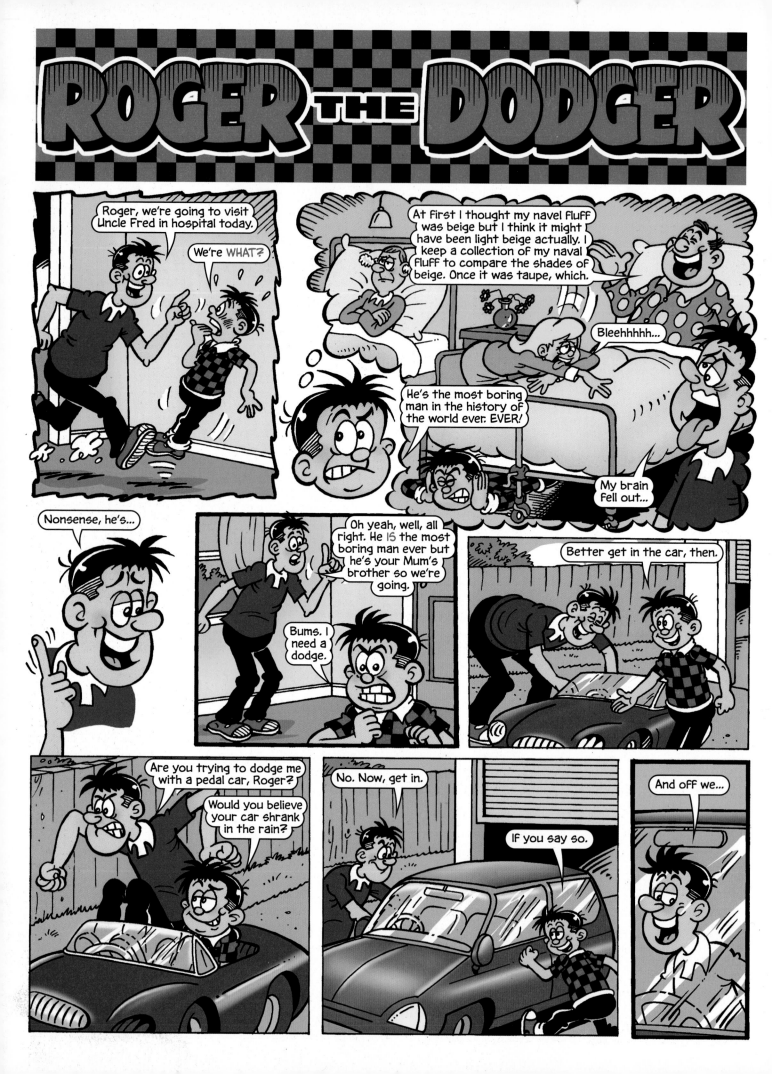

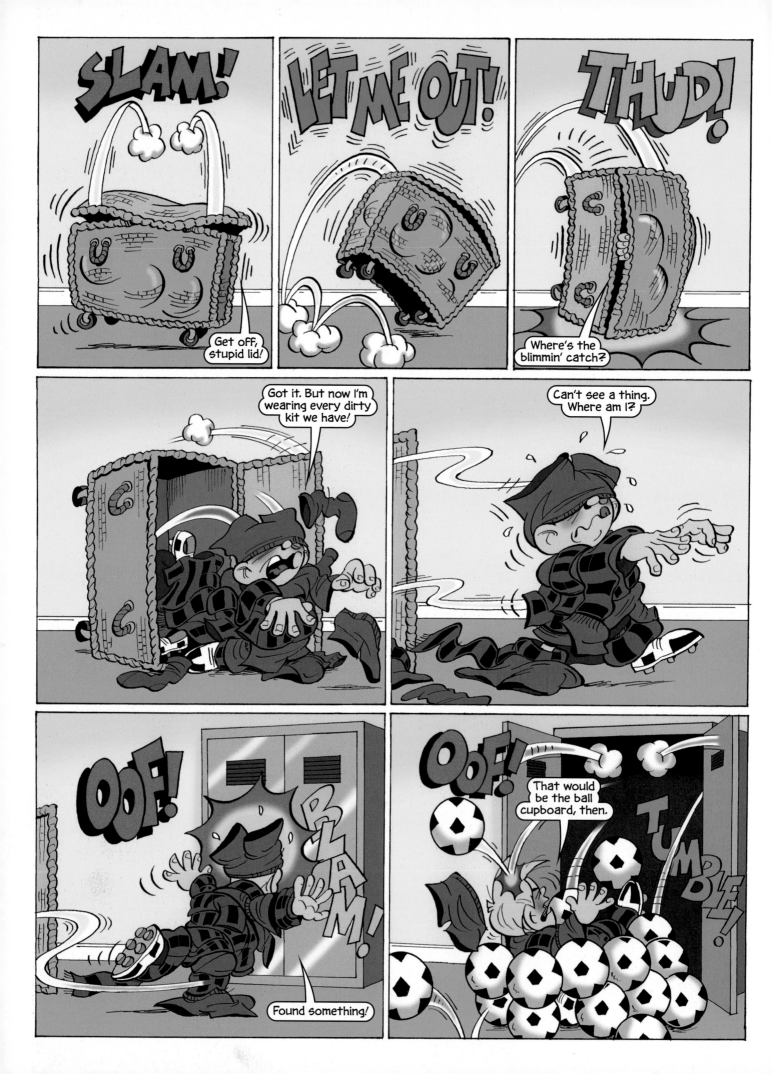

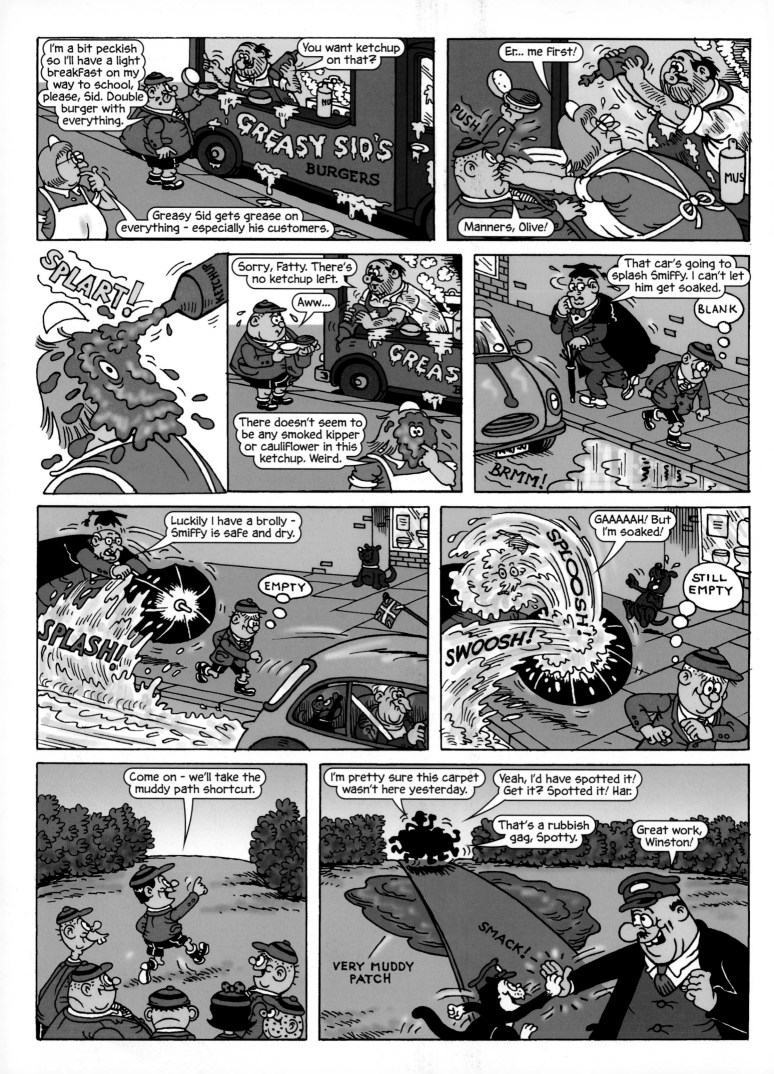

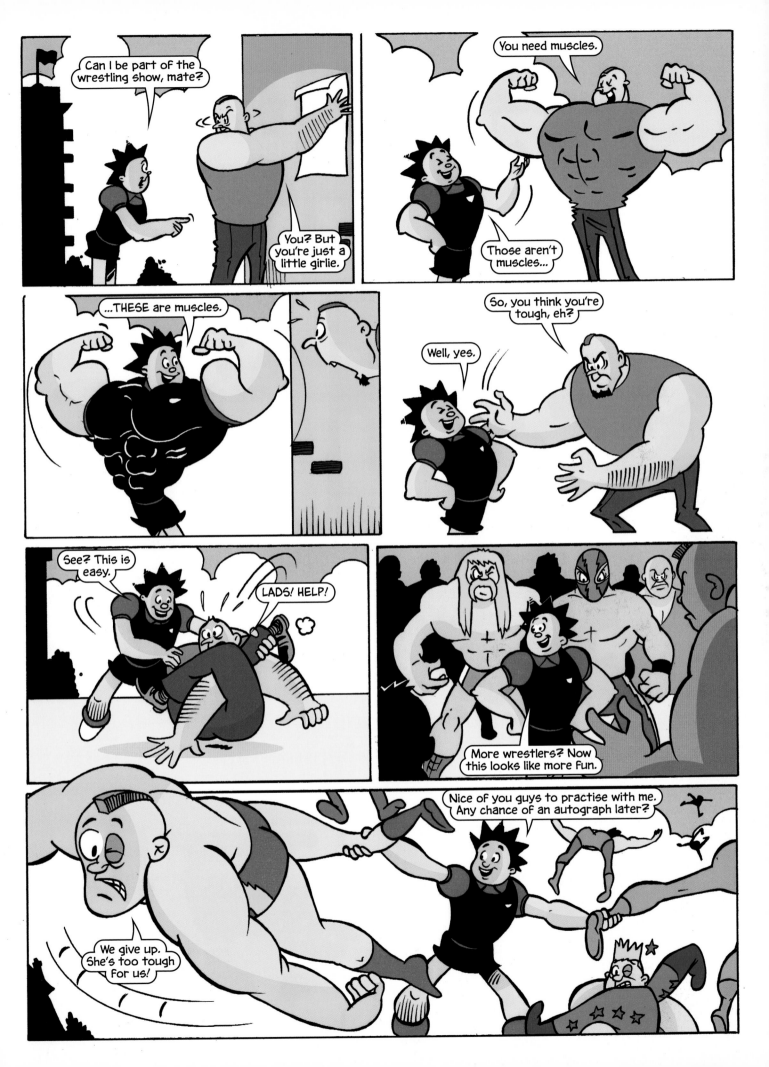

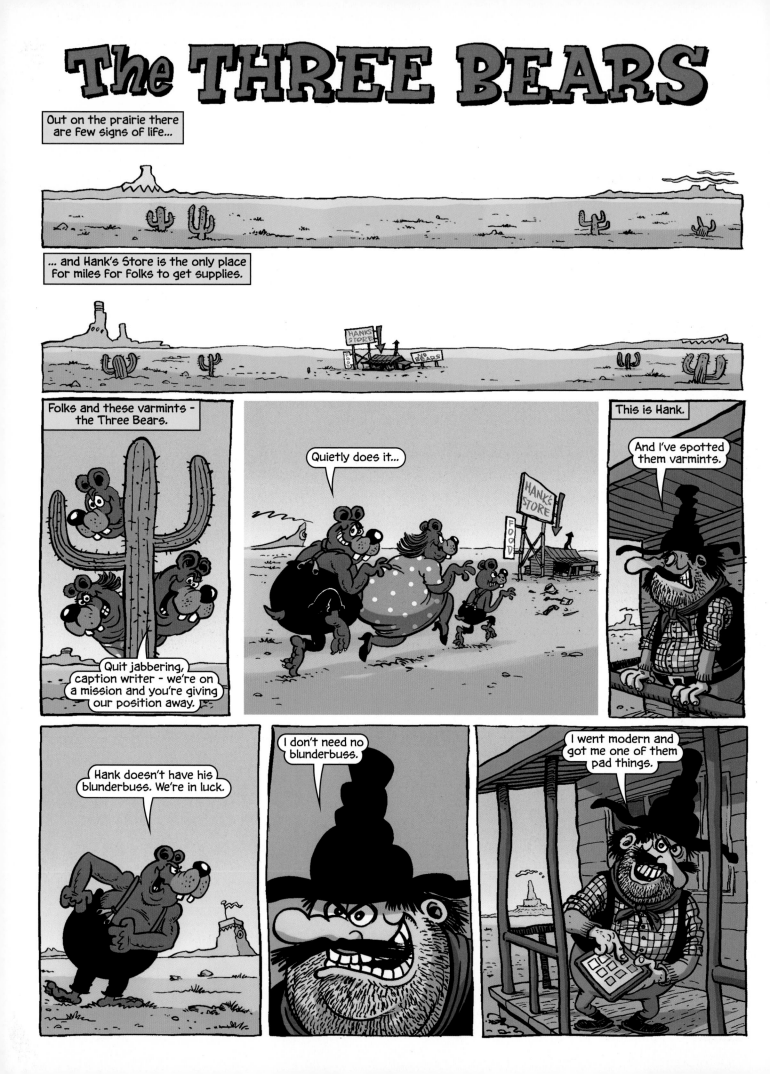

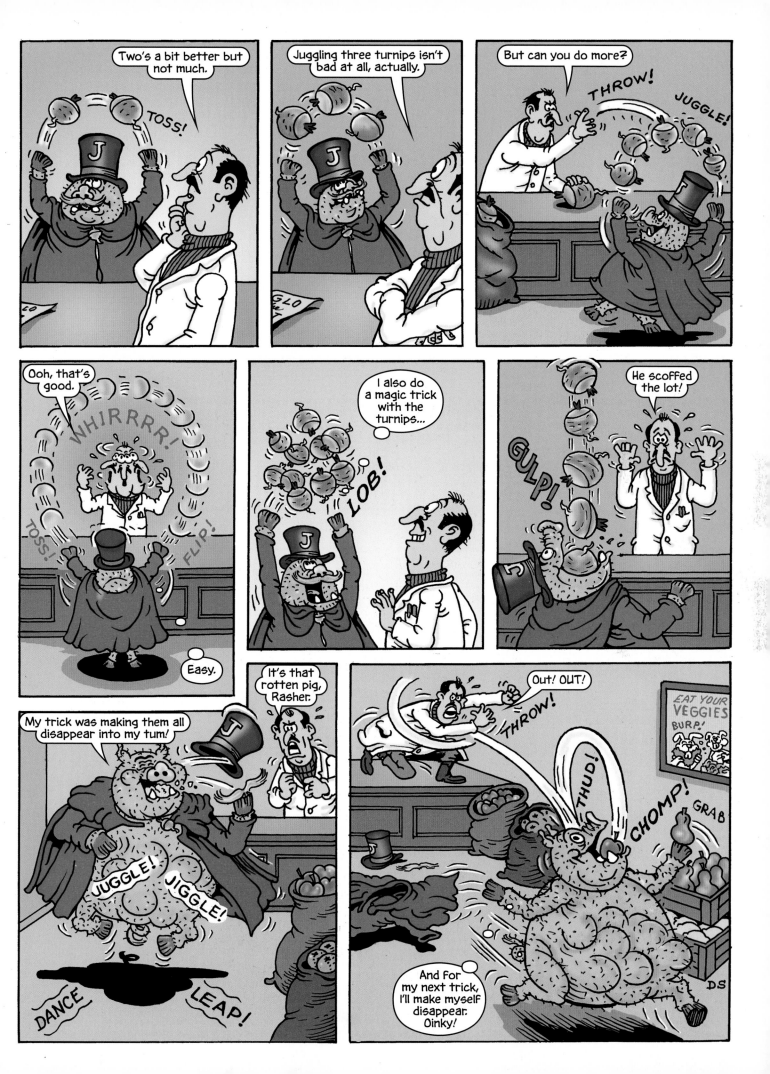

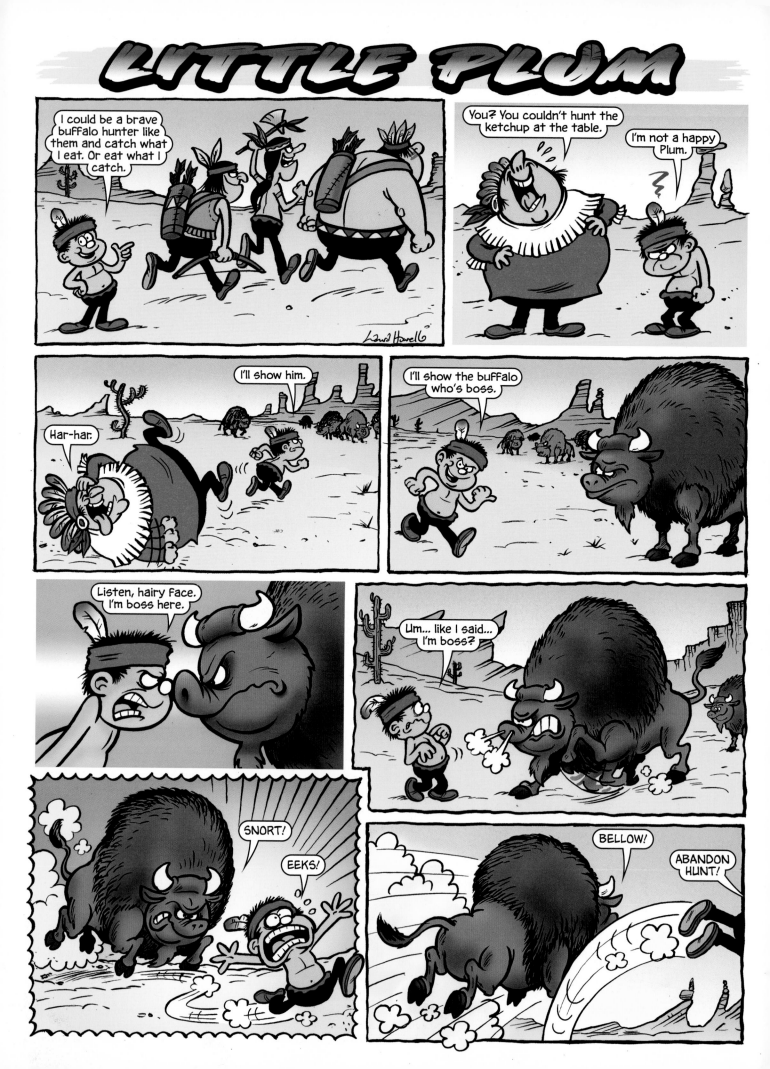

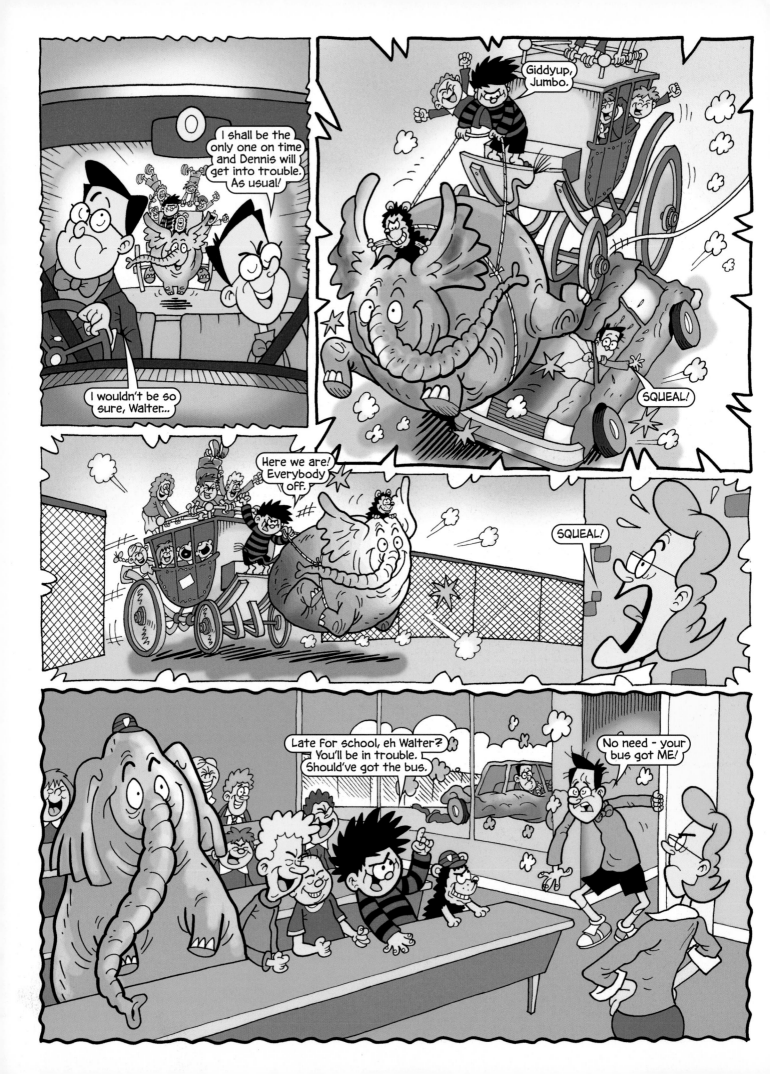

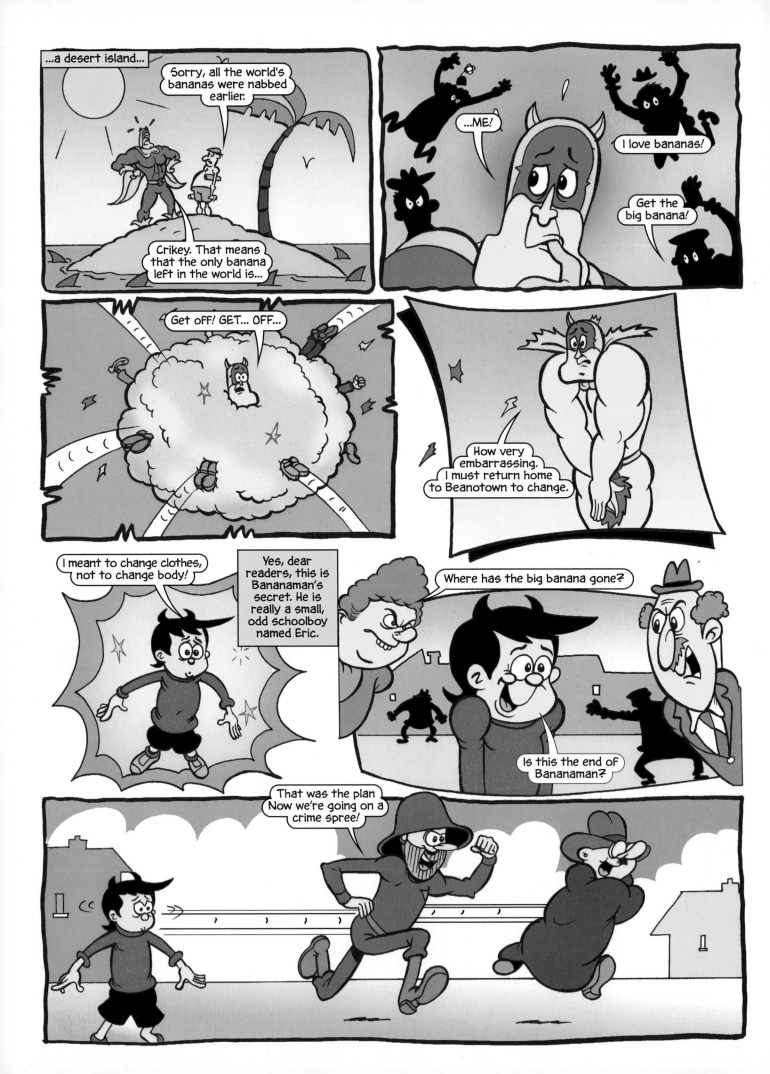

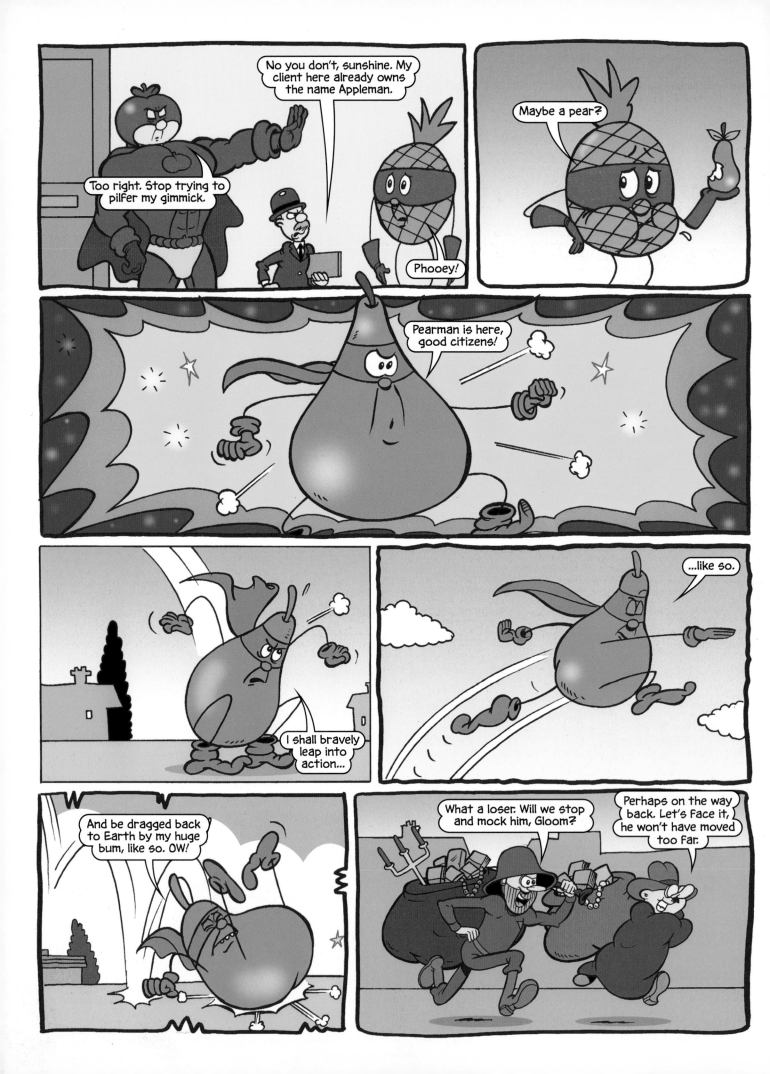

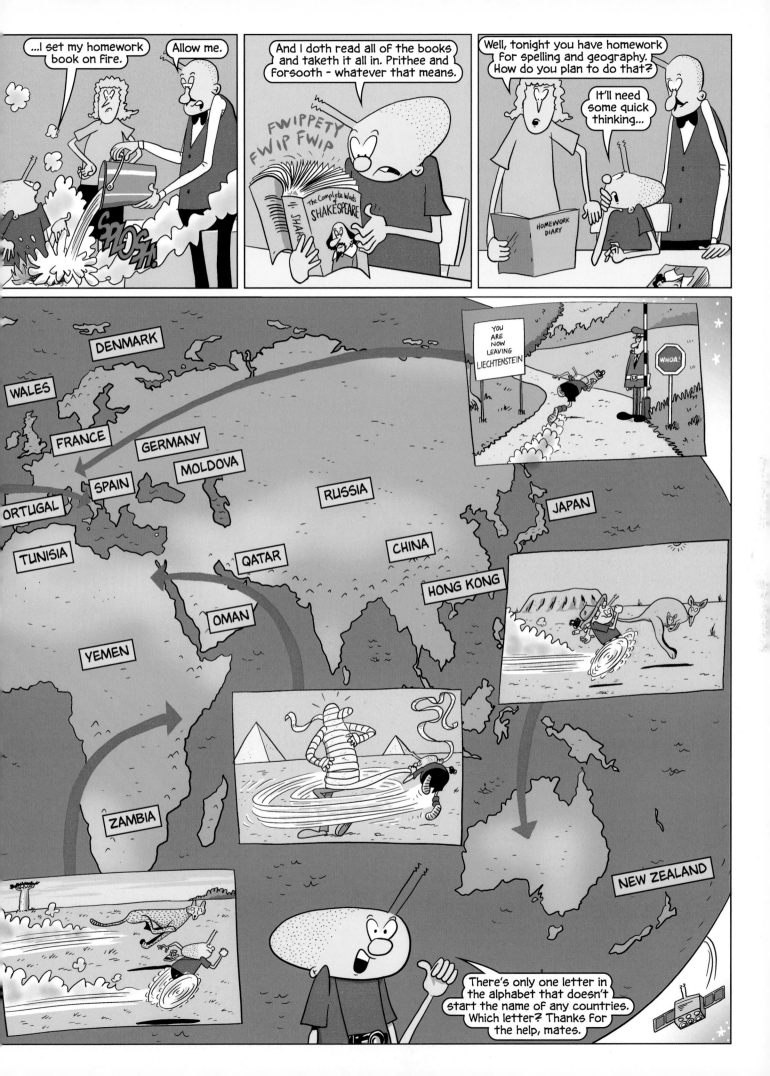

FATTY'S FUN
I love my grub, and I love a laugh too. I'm mixing my two favourite things - jokes and food. Woo-hoo!
Two muffins are baking in an oven. One of the muffins says, "Man, is it hot in here!" The other muffin says, "Blimey!!! A talking muffin!"
What do frogs like to drink? Croak-a-cola!
A man walks into A&E with a carrot poking out of his eye, a sausage coming out of his nose, and a banana in his ear. The doctor examines him and says, "Nurse! This man hasn't been eating properly!"
How can you tell if an elephant has been in the refrigerator? Footprints in the butter.

FOODY NIES

Why did the chef get arrested? He was caught beating an egg.

Why do they only eat one egg for breakfast in France? Because in France, one egg is un oeuf!

What do you call a cow with two legs? Lean beef.

What do you get when you cross a chicken with a centipede? About a hundred drumsticks!

PEAS

What's the difference between pea soup and roast beef? Well, anyone can roast beef!

Knock, knock.
Who's there?
Banana?
Banana who?
Knock, knock.
Who's there?
Banana?
Banana who?
Knock, knock.
Who's there?
Banana?
Banana who?
Knock, knock
Who's there?
Orange.
Orange who?
Orange you glad I didn't say banana?

What happened when the butcher sat on his meat slicer? He got a little behind in his work.

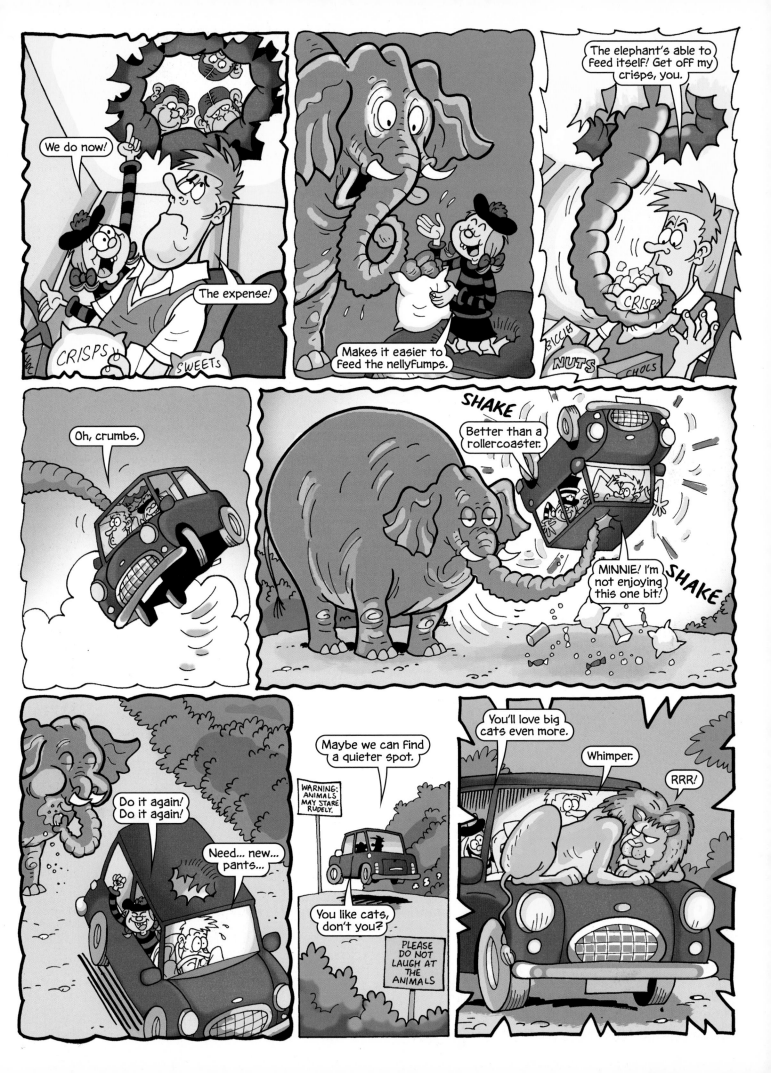

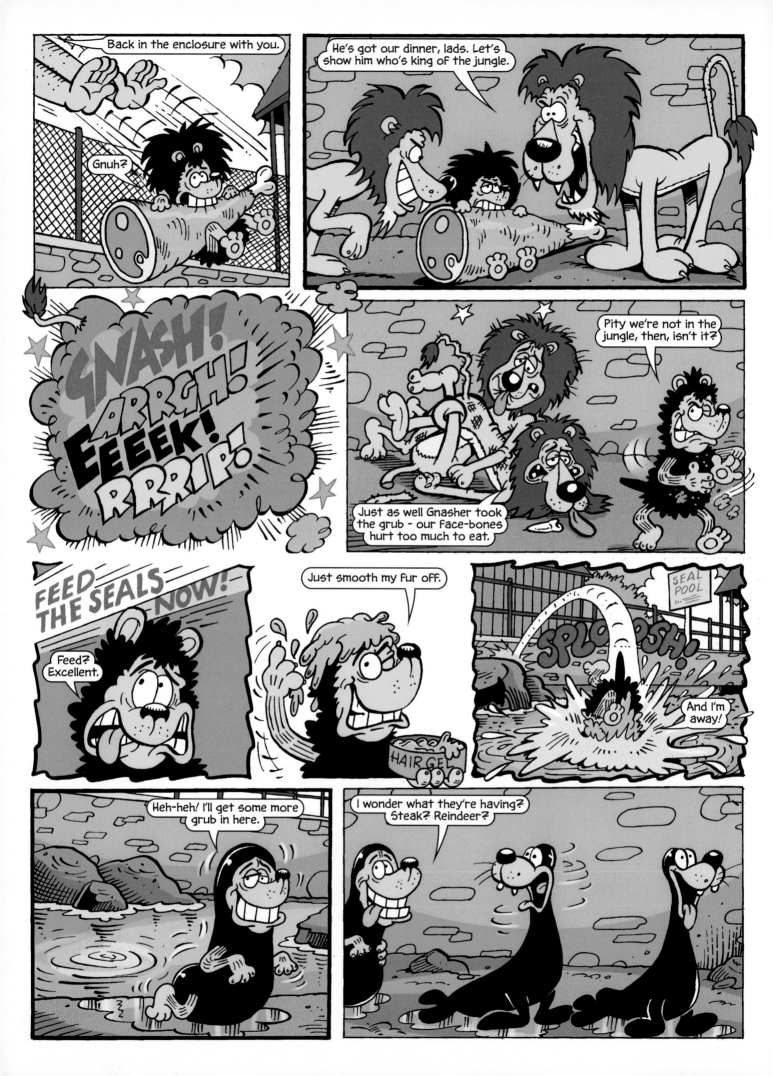

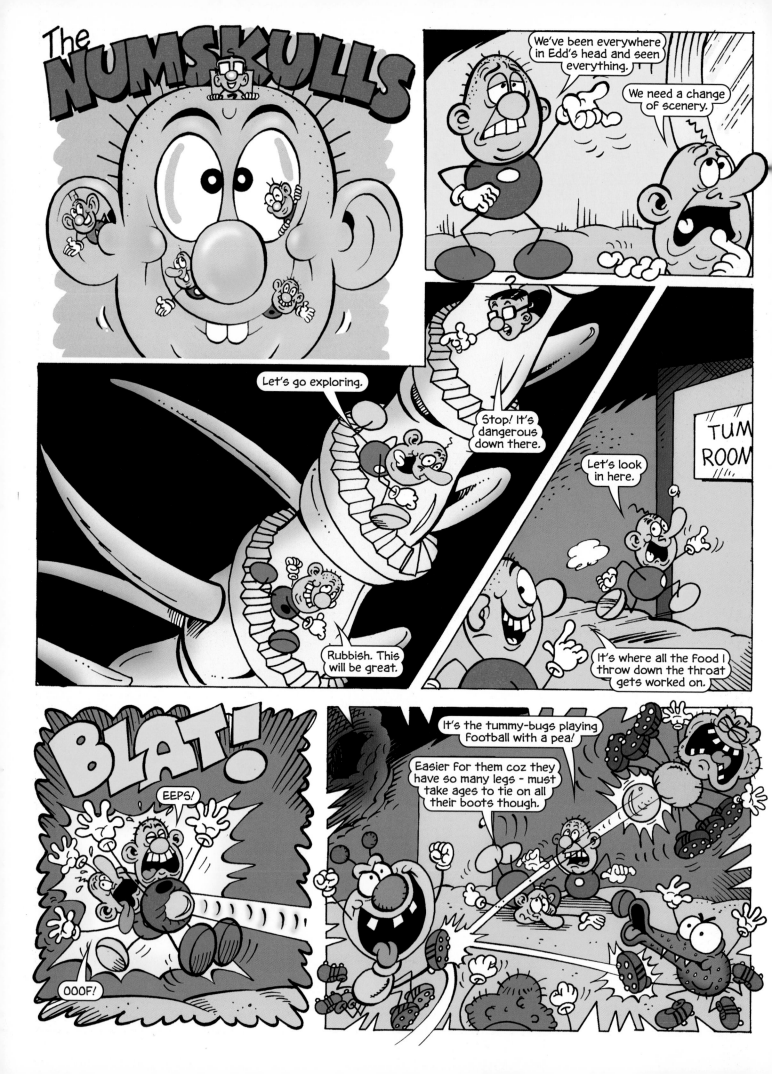

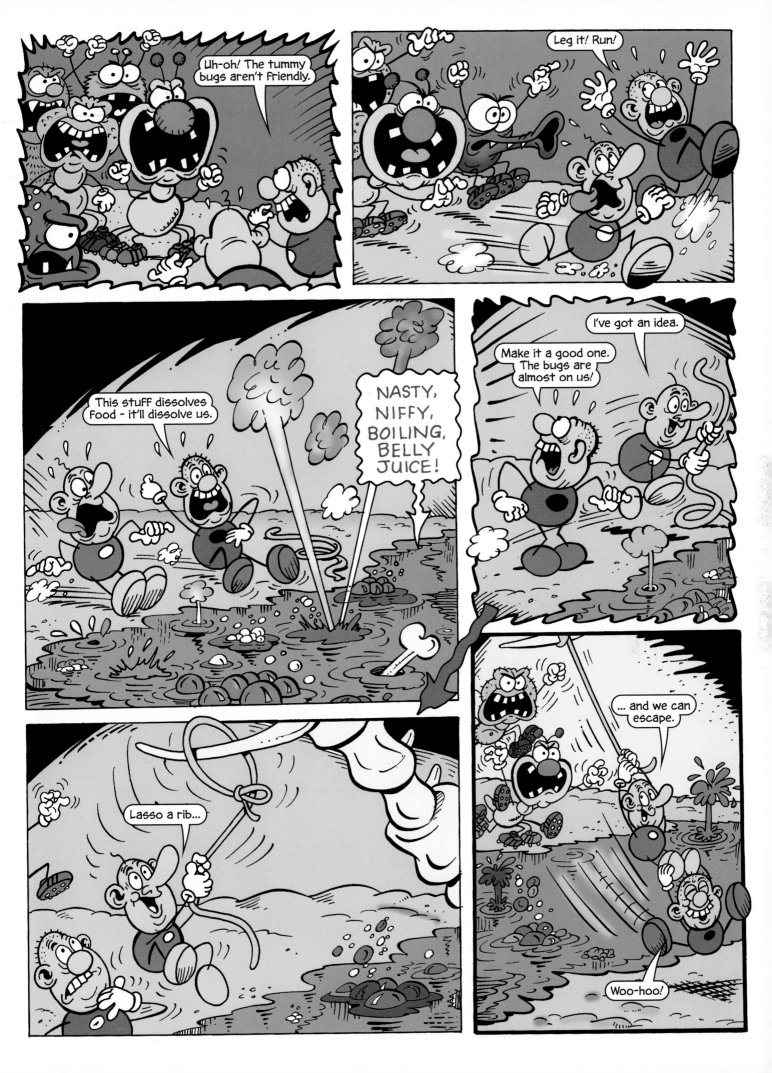

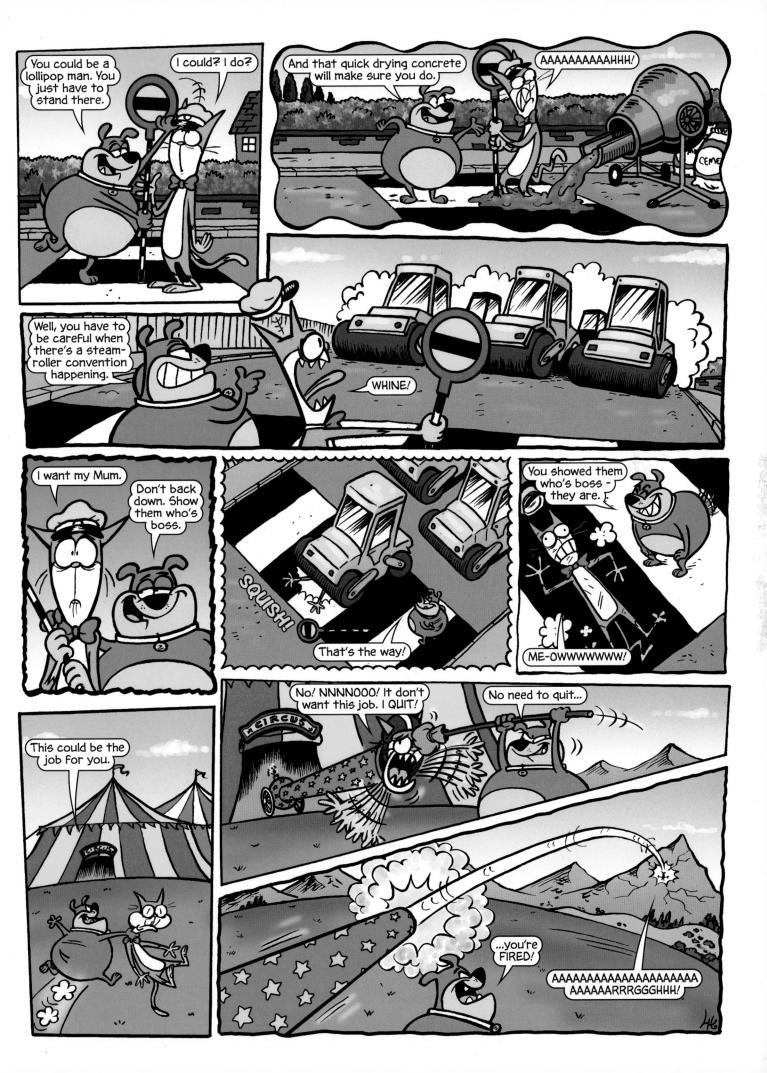

Pete's Science Project

Pete hated homework. Well, who doesn't? It's horrible, isn't it?

And that was why just after tea-time one Sunday, Pete answered "Nope!" when asked if he had done his homework. In fact, he not only hadn't done it yet, he had no intention of doing it at all. He was a bright lad and he was sure he would come up with a good enough excuse for not doing his homework.

Unfortunately, just this once, Pete's Dad was still awake. Usually a nice Sunday dinner and football on TV kept his dad busy, but not this Sunday.

After a lot of searching, Pete found his homework book at the bottom of his schoolbag. It was covered with mud from his sports socks, fluff from his towels and crumbs and bits of crisps from his lunches. He opened it. There, in his own bored handwriting, written on Friday afternoon as he had waited for the last bell of the school week to finally ring, were two words that made his heart sink.

Science Project

Science project? That rang a bell. He hadn't really been paying attention in class. Well, he never really paid attention in class, but that science project thing did sound a little bit familiar. Was he supposed to have done a science project? Oh, dear!

He only had an hour before bedtime to finish the project,

and he had his dopey Dad there making sure he didn't skip homework for once. What could he do? A moon rocket? A time machine? And then Pete's sneaky little mind clicked with an idea. He didn't have to make anything that worked. He just had to make something, then he could pretend that it worked. Or maybe it didn't have to work at all. Lots of big scientific experiments failed, didn't they?

Yes, that was the plan. All he had to do was cobble together some kind of gadget using whatever he could find in the house and pretend it was a great invention for his experiment, and then sit back and watch nothing happen.

But what was in the house that he could use? Well, there were mirrors. They would look good. After all, experiments were usually quite shiny, weren't they? Mum had an old lava lamp and Dad had a battery shaver. Grandad's big beatbox radio and CD player from the 1980s would be a useful control deck. The CDs would look good if they were spinning...

And so Pete went scavenging through his house, picking up anything he thought might look good in his invention. Dad's food mixer, Mum's electric toothbrush, anything at all that he could find. And soon it was all being stuck together. Mirrors around the outside, reflecting light from the CDs that spun inside, with the lava lamp at the very centre and all the other bits and bobs moving and grinding. Pete's science project looked like a proper invention. Nobody would know that it would do nothing at all, but at least it looked like an invention.

Pete was rather pleased with himself. He had worked out a way to avoid doing real homework and still stay out of trouble at school, and he had done it all with fifteen minutes to spare before bed-time.

But, sadly for Pete, his Mum and Dad both wanted to see what his invention did. So Pete turned on his machine and it started to spin and whirr, flash and clang. Both of his parents were very impressed. "But what does it actually do?" asked Dad.

"What does it do?" Pete asked. "Isn't it obvious? I'd have thought anybody could tell that."

Dad coughed and flustered. Mum flustered and coughed. She liked to be different. "We can see what it does," Mum said uncertainly. "We just wondered if you might like to tell us more."

Pete pointed to the spinning CDs and the reflected light. "The oscillating light reverses the polarity of the neutron flow and discombobulates the hoijamaflip. And, of course, the electromagnetic do-hickey nirdles the bathosphere." He

sounded so confident and knowledgeable. His parents had no idea that he was picking random words from his memory.

"So," Dad said uncertainly. "Is that worth anything?"

"Oh, yes," Pete said. "It could make a million pounds." "A million pounds?" Dad's eyes were glassy with greed. "I wish I had a million pounds."

Pete's machine wheezed and groaned, and then after a bright flash of light, hundreds of ten pound notes sprayed out of the machine. Dad's jaw dropped to the floor. Mum's followed a few seconds later. She didn't like to be outdone.

"I wish I had a million pounds, too," Mum said, and as Dad greedily scooped up the tenners, another million pounds sprayed out at Mum.

Pete just stared. His parents had each asked for a million pounds and sure enough, they had both received a million pounds from the machine he had invented. Did his machine grant wishes? Had he accidentally invented a wish machine? There was only one way to find out. "I wish I had an ice cream."

With a flash, an ice cream arrived. Pete smiled. He did have a wish machine. And then he scowled. "I wish I had the biggest ice cream ever." There was another flash and Pete

had the biggest ice cream in the world. Normally his parents would have objected to an ice cream this close to bed-time but they were running wild with wishes. New shoes, fancy cars, expensive jewellery, designer clothes... the machine was spitting them out as fast as the parents could ask for them. After a few minutes, Pete's room was full of the most expensive things his parents could imagine.

"That's not a problem," Mum said gleefully. "I wish we had a bigger house."

And with a flash, they were in a bigger house. A mansion with a golden chandelier and a swimming pool outside.

"But we're in the same street," complained Dad. "I wish we were somewhere hotter."

Another flash took them to the middle of a desert. "Too hot," complained Mum.

Pete didn't care. The parents could move the house anywhere they wanted. This was his chance to have something he always wanted. "I wish I had a pet," he said. With a flash, a goldfish in a bowl appeared in the room. "Rubbish," said Pete. "I wish I had a nice, big hairy pet!" The machine flashed again and a woolly mammoth trumpeted out, waving its trunk in a friendly manner.

"Mars?" shrieked Mum. "How will we get you to school in the morning?"

Dad dived back behind his golden chair to avoid the Mammoth's trunk as it ran by, and to avoid being munched by the T Rex, which was looking very peckish. The dinosaur didn't see Dad, but its beady eyes did catch sight of Pete, and it licked its lips.

"Oh, crumbs," Pete squeaked. "I wish I'd never invented that stupid machine."

Dad shrieked and yelled. "I wish something would get rid of that hairy elephant!"

The machine had barely flashed when a blood-curdling roar filled the room and a Tyrannosaurus Rex lumbered out. Its eyes fixed on the mammoth and it started chasing the hairy beast around the house.

Through the sound of smashing and crashing, Pete heard his mum scream, "I wish somebody would get rid of those animals." Moments later a group of cavemen all holding spears appeared in a flash of light and immediately started chasing the two monsters.

"I wish we were far away from here," Dad yelled from behind his new solid gold reclining chair.

There was yet another flash and the house disappeared from the desert... and reappeared in another, only this time under a pink sky. It took Pete a moment to realise what had happened. "Oh, no," he said. "We're on Mars!"

There was a giant flash and suddenly Pete and his parents were back in their house, their original house, with no machine, no millions of pounds or sports cars or slavering dinosaurs. Dad blinked, as if trying to remember something, and then shrugged. "So, Pete," he said. "Have you done your homework?"

Pete gulped. "Yes," he said loudly.

"And it was so dangerous I'm never doing homework again!"

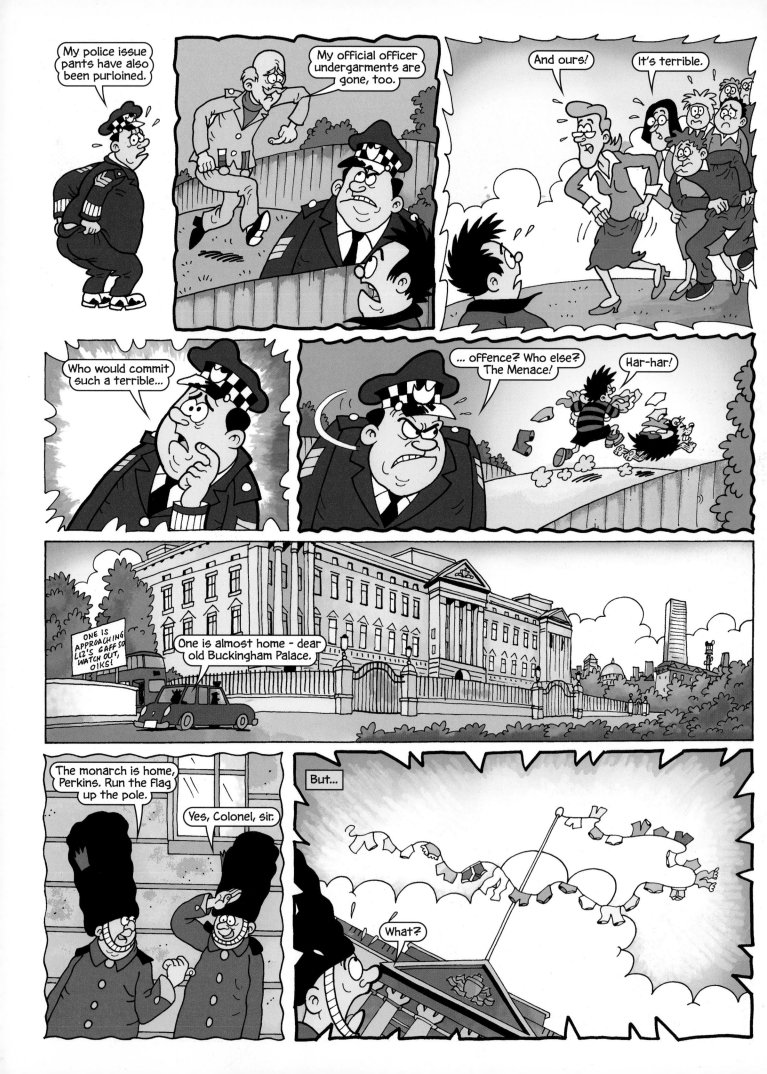